Let there be a world

by FELIX GREENE

G000154992

FOREWORD This book in its original form was written nearly twenty years ago. We were living in the United States at the time and tests of atomic and nuclear bombs were still being conducted in the atmosphere with horrendous consequences. No American publisher was ready to take the responsibility of issuing the book, so my wife and I (with the help of Hubert Leckie, a brilliant designer from Washington, D.C.) published it ourselves. We knew that the book would be attacked, so the facts we presented were checked carefully by noted scientists and biologists.

The book "caught on", and every day we packed the orders in our garage and mailed them out. Eventually we packed and sent off over 85,000 copies. A well-wisher sent a copy to every member of the U.S. Congress.

Much has changed in the intervening years, and though tests in the atmosphere were ended in the United States and the Soviet Union (but not in some other countries) the world has moved very much closer to the brink of total disaster. We have made a few changes in this edition to bring the material up to date, but otherwise the book is substantially the same as the original edition.

Our thoughts, too, have undergone changes during the past twenty years. Uniting with others to protest against the armaments race on as wide a scale as possible is necessary and very important. But I have come to realize, as many others have, that protest alone is not enough to alter the extraordinary crisis which confronts us; that a wholly *new approach in our thinking* is necessary. So I have added a personal postscript which outlines in brief what I believe individuals can do about this enormous problem of human survival.

Felix Greene

FALL-OUT VERSUS LIFE

2,O

OOO,OOO YEARS AGO...

. . . by divine intent, by chance molecular association or by some process that is still beyond our understanding, the first cell came into being and on this lifeless planet, life began. Not a single cell alone, but a cell that became two cells, which in turn became four, and those four eight. . . .

All life today is still based on the single cell which divides itself and multiplies. Whether it be the petal of a flower or a tiger's tooth, the wing of a butterfly or the substance of our brain, the basic unit is the cell forever dividing and renewing itself.

This is the unbroken thread that links us to a far distant past, this is the life process of which we humans are a part.

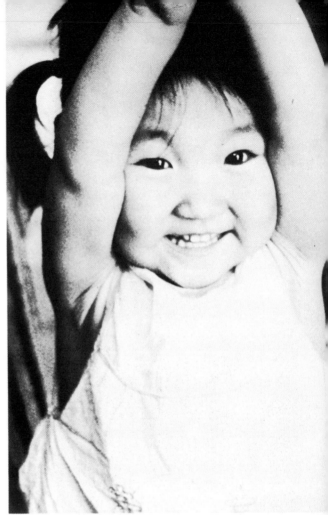

The nature of these children is largely determined by the genes they have inherited from their parents.

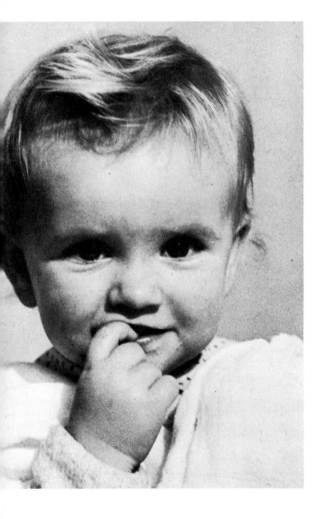

The genes they have inherited are their link with two thousand million years of evolution.

Genes are very small. If all the genes inherited by every human being living today were put together they would form a sphere no larger than the head of a pin.

This tiny sphere represents the total pool of germ plasm that would determine the future development of the entire human race.

Genes are molecules and can be injured by radiation.

All scientists agree that every test of a nuclear weapon increases the radiation our bodies are absorbing. Radioactive dust falls to earth and passes into our bodies when we eat vegetables or drink milk.

Because of the bomb tests still being carried out by some countries no child anywhere in the world can drink milk that is free of poison caused by radioactive fall-out.

If this spot were radioactive you would feel nothing . . . but the genes that you pass on to your children might be damaged.

If some of your genes have been damaged your children could be born dead, mentally incapacitated, deformed . . . . or blind.

WHOM SHALL WE BELIEV

Some officials tell us that radiation dangers from fall-out are less than the dangers from a luminous watch—but in the United States the sale of luminous pocket watches with radium illuminated dials is prohibited because of the danger their radiation might cause.

The Federal Radiation Council has stated: "It is virtually certain that genetic effects can be produced by even the lowest doses." And the United Nations Scientific Committee on the Effects of Atomic Radiation has urged that all nuclear tests should cease, to prevent genetic damage which may continue for many generations.

We do not know exactly how many people have died or are dying because of the tests already carried out.

We do not know exactly how many children not yet born will be born defective or dead because of the testing of nuclear weapons.

We do know that the tests already carried out will produce harmful effects for the next 10,000 years if the human race survives.

We do know that some world-famous scientists have estimate that the tests already carried out may ultimately produce one million seriously defective children.

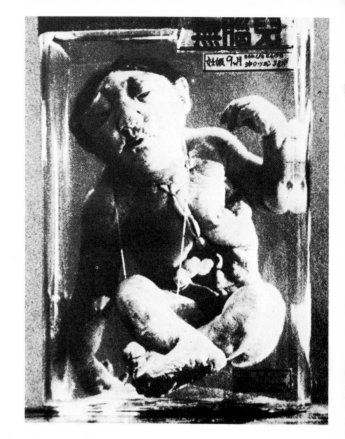

The mothers of these babies survived the bombing at Nagasaki but their babies were born deformed and dead. After autopsy their bodies were preserved to show others what may happen when genes are damaged by nuclear radiation.

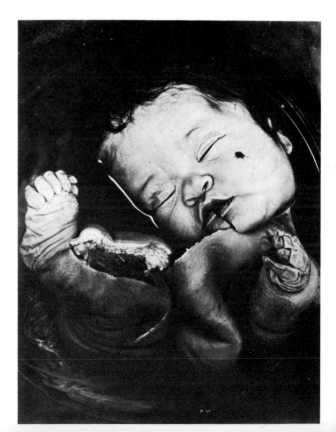

Only those who have never been present at the birth of a deformed baby, never witnessed the whimpering shock of its mother, dare to say that nuclear tests should be continued.

DR ALBERT SCHWEITZER

TH

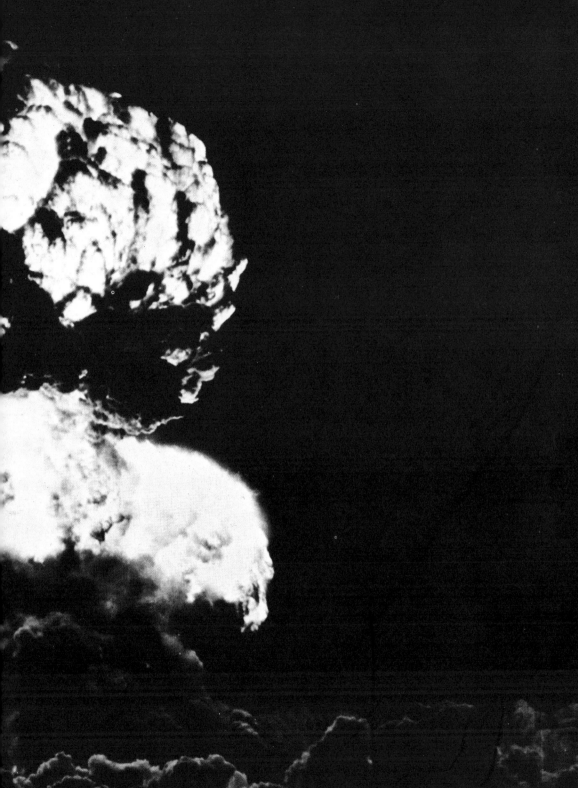

OMB VERSUS CIVILIZATION

All that we are, all that our civilization has accomplished, has arisen from the past.

United States of starting a new round in the nuclear arms race. The Soviets threatened to retaliate with a massive test series of their own, which they are suspected of already preparing. The cancellation of our tests deprives them of any propagandistic pretext for resuming theirs.

But cancellation is not enough. Even more determined eff[...] present deadloc[...] new and powerf[...] 27 distinguished[...] laureates. They[...] gress and the [...] as being in th[...] States and of [...] this newspaper, that the risk of continuing the arms race without a test-ban treaty is considerably greater than the risk that a ban might be violated by secret testing. For such a treaty would stop immediately all above-ground tests; and though some uncertainty might remain regarding underground tests, these have been found of lesser military value. Detection techniques are already such as to make it too risky for the Soviets to cheat. The treaty might not last, but as long as it lasts, it would leave our nuclear deterrent capacity intact, reduce the speed of the armament race, help to inhibit the spread of nuclear arms, reduce the likelihood

pres[...] answ[...] who [...] Mr. [...] that [...] mista[...] to ru[...]

he neve[...] the cit[...] Wel[...] stance[...] and w[...] Demo[...] viser,[...] the v[...] in Ne[...] Bu[...] in po[...] party[...] 1962,[...] By 1[...]

Whoever we are, wherever we live, we are part of an historical proces

that far outspans our own generation.

For the first time in history we who live today have the power to bring all civilization to an end.

JAPAN 1945...

In Hiroshima, on Monday morning the sixth of August, after the markets were open and when people were on their way to work, a single atom bomb was dropped from a high altitude. The bomb measured only 28 inches by 120 inches, and it floated slowly down attached to a parachute.

At 2,200 feet it exploded.

. . . and three days later, Nagasaki.

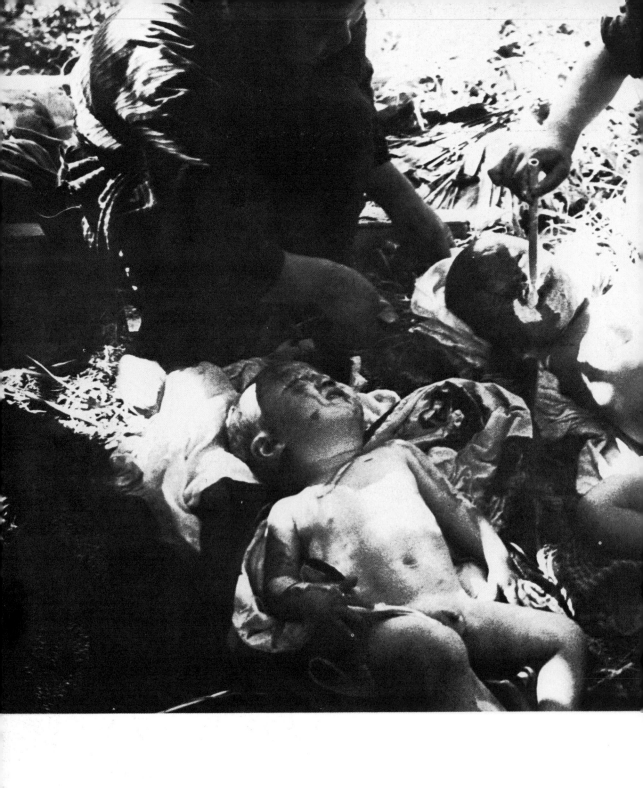

Some survived . . .

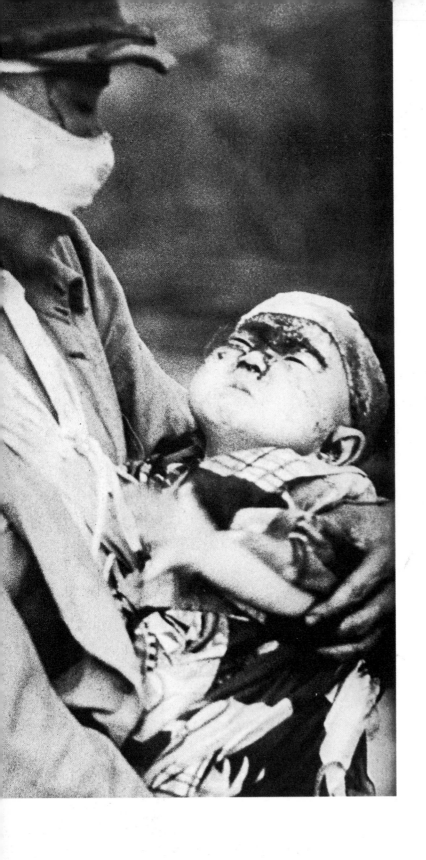

Some survived to die later.

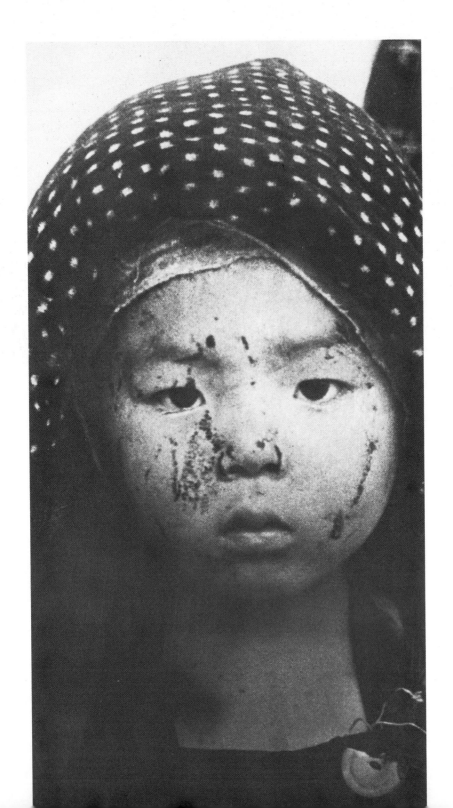

Humanity is outraged in me and with me. We must not dissimulate nor try to forget this indignation which is one of the most passionate forms of love.

GEORGE SAND

THE MANHATTAN PROJECT ATOMIC BOMB INVESTIGATING GROUP

THE ATTACKS

Hiroshima

Hiroshima was the primary target of the first atomic bomb mission. The mission went smoothly in every respect. The weather was good, and the crew and equipment functioned perfectly. In every detail, the attack was carried out exactly as planned, and the bomb performed exactly as expected.

The bomb exploded over Hiroshima at 8:15 on the morning of August 6, 1945. About an hour previously, the Japanese early warning radar net had detected the approach of some American aircraft headed for the southern part of Japan. The alert had been given and radio broadcasting stopped in many cities, among them Hiroshima. The planes approached the coast at a very high altitude. At nearly 8:00 A.M., the radar operator in Hiroshima determined that the number of planes coming in was very small - probably not more than three - and the air raid alert was lifted. The normal radio broadcast warning was given to the people that it might be advisable to go to shelter if B-29's were actually sighted, but no raid was expected beyond some sort of reconnaissance. At 8:15 A.M., the bomb exploded with a blinding flash in the sky, and a great rush of air and a loud rumble of noise extended for many miles around the city; the first blast was soon followed by the sounds of falling buildings and of growing fires, and a great cloud of dust and smoke began to cast a pall of darkness over the city.

. . . ed concr . . .
burned or blown away; the casualties in such buildings near the center of explosion were almost 100%. In Hiroshima fires sprang up simultaneously all over the wide flat central area of the city; these fires soon combined in an immense "fire storm" (high winds blowing inwards toward the center of a large conflagration) similar to those caused by ordinary mass incendiary raids; the resulting terrific conflagration burned out almost everything which had not already been destroyed by the blast in a roughly circular area of 4.4 square miles around the point directly under the explosion (this point will hereafter in this report be referred to as X). Similar fires broke out in Nagasaki, but no devastating fire storm resulted as in Hiroshima because of the irregular shape of the city.

. . . were instantly and completely devastated. 66,00 . . .
people were killed, and 69,000 injured.

On August 9th, three days later, at 11:02 A.M., another B-29 dropped the second bomb on the industrial section of the city of Nagasaki, totally destroying 1½ square miles of the city, killing 39,000 persons, and injuring 25,000 more.

On August 10, the day after the atomic bombing of Nagasaki, the Japanese . . . ted that it be permitt . . . r under the terms of the . . . July 26th . . .

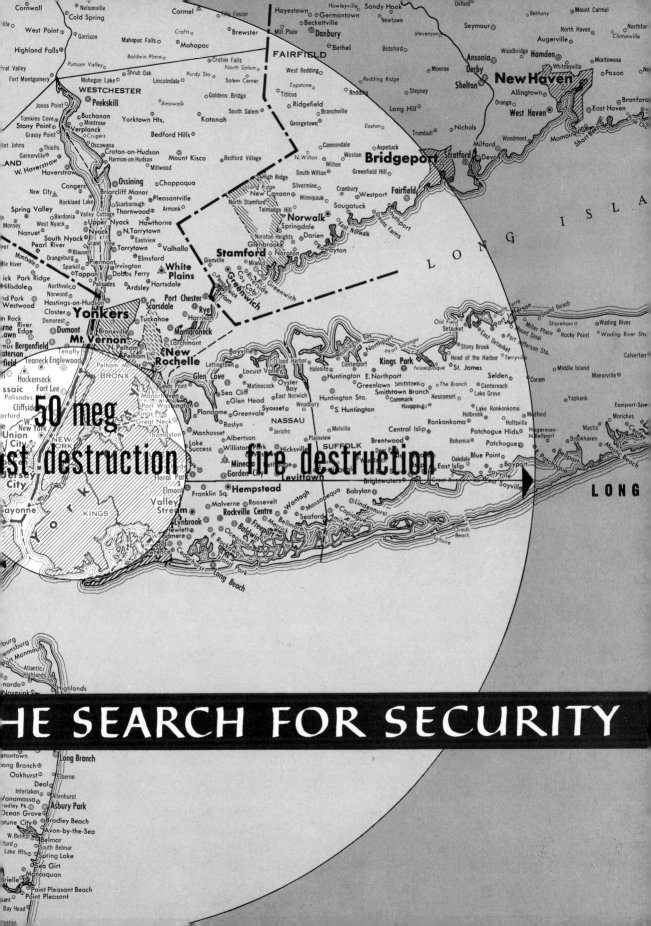

50 meg
st destruction

fire destruction

oday's bombs are at least 2,500 times more powerful than the bomb which was dropped on Hiroshima. A ngle H-bomb on New York could kill most people in the city by blast, fire and radiation. Nearly everyone ithin fifty miles would be killed by local fall-out.

The governments of the wo

ling $10 million *per minute* for military "security"—and we have never before been less secure.

We pay for a single fighter plane with half a million bushels of wheat. . . . Is there no othe

world can live?

WIGHT D. EISENHOWER

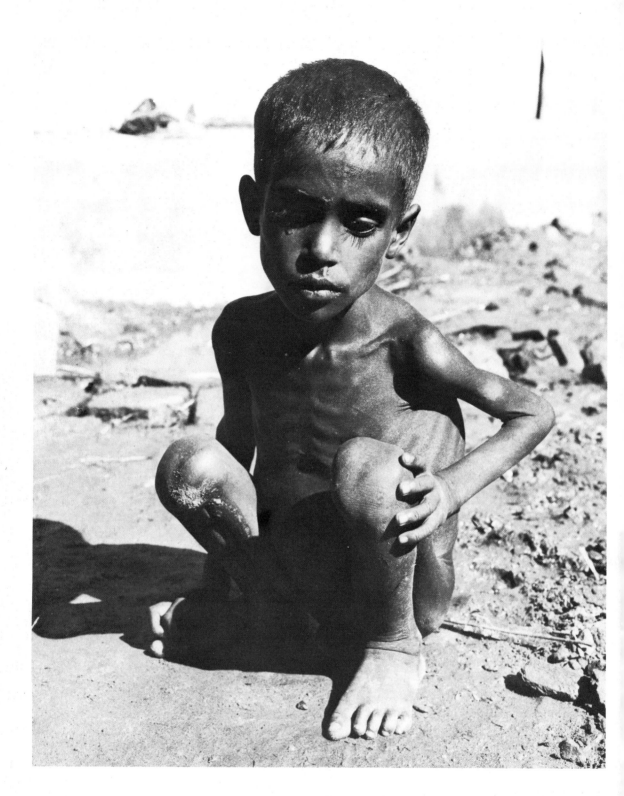

. . . and one third of the world is hungry all the time.

FOR THE FIRST TIME IN HISTORY

we have the knowledge and resources to transform utterly the conditions of life on this planet. With the money, ingenuity, intelligence and energy that the world now expends on preparing for war, advances hitherto undreamed of are now within our reach.

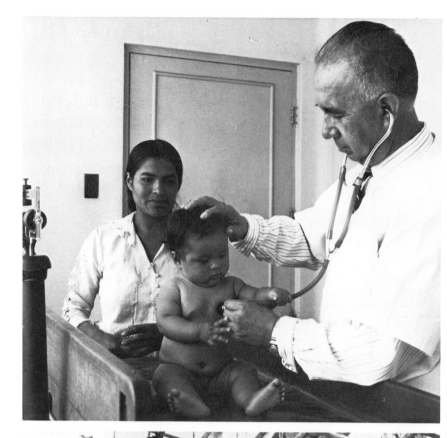

Slums can be cleared, water can be brought to deserts,
highways can be thrust through jungles. Hospitals,
schools, playgrounds, parks, can be built on a scale
beyond imagination. Within a generation hunger,
disease and illiteracy might be things of the past, and
the·story of mankind would have a new and
extraordinary beginning.

SOME FACTS ABOUT MODERN WEAPONS

THE OLD AND THE NEW

A World War II "blockbuster" was equivalent to 1 ton of TNT. A World War II heavy air raid was equivalent to 1,000 tons of TNT. Hydrogen bombs of up to 90 megatons (90,000,000 tons of TNT) have been tested.

> A single 57 megaton bomb has the equivalent explosive power of a heavy 1,000 ton World War II air raid continued every day for 156 years

DELIVERY

Missiles can carry strategic nuclear warheads 6,000 miles in less than half an hour. Fired from the other side of the world they are accurate to within a few hundred feet of their target.

NEW WEAPONS

The British Government has decided to buy the Trident submarine and missile system from the Americans. It will cost the British people at least £6,000 million.

A Trident submarine

> With this money Britain could:
> - build 500,000 new homes.
> - double the number of hospitals in Britain.
> - increase the state old age pension to £560 per week.
> - electrify all British railway lines eight times over.

THE CRUISE MISSILE

NATO has decided that Britain should ~~buy~~ *station* 160 Cruise Missiles. The decision was taken without the consultation of Parliament, and the missiles, although sited in England, will be entirely under the control of the United States. Each Cruise Missile carries a 20 kiloton warhead—equivalent to 10 Hiroshima bombs.

A Cruise Missile

NEUTRON WEAPONS

These are specifically designed for use in Europe. They are designed so that the blast effects are minimized and the radiation effects are enhanced. This means that they destroy people but cause less damage to property.

A U.S. "Lance" missile capable of carrying a neutron weapon

LET THERE BE A WORLD
Erratum
Page 52   THE CRUISE MISSILE
first line should read:
Nato has decided that Britain should station 160 Cruise Missiles.

SS20s

Although the Russians possess fewer missiles and warheads than the western powers they have recently been arming at an alarming rate on land and sea. The weapons that most worry NATO are the SS20 missiles. These have a range of 3000 miles and the Russians are believed to have about 200 now in service, of which 60 per cent are targeted on Europe and the rest on Japan and China.

Missiles in Red Square

NERVE GASES

Soldiers would be better protected than civilians

Both the United States and the Soviet Union are now manufacturing and stockpiling biological and chemical weapons, which may prove to be more deadly to humans even than the nuclear bomb. These gases are stored in cylinders in liquid form and then released from shells or bombs as a cloud of vapour. U.S. officials have admitted that these gases must be stockpiled near the area of military operations—which means they must be stockpiled in Britain and the continental countries.

Modern nerve gases can be absorbed into the body through the skin or mouth. They disrupt the function of the nervous system. The resulting symptoms include intense sweating, contraction of the throat filling the lungs with mucus, vomiting and finally paralysis and death. Death may be a lingering and indescribably painful process.

> The American Joint Chiefs of Staff currently estimate that if chemical weapons were introduced into a European war, nerve gas would soon be used by both sides at a rate of approximately 2,000 tons *a day. One thousandth of a gram is enough to kill a human being.*

WORLD WAR III

In a recent British Civil Defence exercise called "Operation Square Leg" Civil Defence experts assumed that Britain had been attacked by a Russian missile strike. They estimated that 125 H-bombs had exploded throughout the U.K. on cities, military targets and American bases. This would be the equivalent of 13,000 bombs of the type that totally destroyed Hiroshima. They estimated that London would be hit by 6 bombs each of 10 megatons or more.

- A 10 megaton bomb exploding in your area would burn everything and everyone within a radius of 10-20 miles.

- It would give off a flash of light and heat quicker than your eyes can blink and would burn the eyes of people looking at it from 200 to 300 miles away. (The eyes of rabbits 300 miles away were burned from the flash of an H-bomb explosion in 1958.)

- It would grow in half a minute into a blinding fireball three miles across and as hot as the inside of the sun.

- It would burn you fatally or very badly up to 22 miles away if you were unprotected.

•It would start a vast number of fires within a 25-mile radius and in a built-up area would almost certainly create a fire-storm.

•A 100 megaton bomb explosion would create a fireball 8 miles across. Brick houses would be destroyed within a circle 34 miles across, and innumerable fires would be started up to sixty miles away.

•The radioactive fall-out from a 100 megaton bomb would be so great that in an area of at least 1,000 square miles anyone unprotected for as long as an hour would die.

•Beyond the area of total destruction, radiation sickness, accompanied by vomiting, bleeding, and convulsions, would kill many people within days. For hundreds of thousands of other people death would take longer. (Radiation increases one's susceptibility to all sorts of infections as well as causing cancer.)

GENETIC EFFECTS The relatively small A-bomb exploded at Hiroshima caused many women to give birth to stillborn or deformed children. The consequences of a general nuclear war would be so much worse that there is really no comparison. Survivors of the blast would in effect be living for days or weeks in a radioactive oven. A nuclear war would leave the survivors with an appalling total of inborn deformities that would continue for many generations. The final toll of a nuclear war might be hundreds of millions of cripples, invalids, and idiots.

STOCKPILES The nuclear powers have now produced more bombs than they can ever use. Five nations have produced 50,000 nuclear weapons all of which have a power many times that of the Hiroshima bomb.

By the 1960s the United States alone had a stockpile of explosives equivalent to 30 tons of TNT *for every man, woman and child in the entire world*. This has been vastly increased since then.

CIVIL DEFENCE Many people who live in large cities imagine that the government has plans to evacuate them, or at least to provide communal shelters. We now know that neither is envisaged. General evacuation schemes have been abandoned. People will now be ordered to stay in their homes even though, in areas such as London, Manchester or Glasgow, this would mean almost certain death.

Those who try, before hostilities begin, to flee from the cities will be held back by the Army and Police. Those who manage to leave their homes for the countryside, will not, by the order of the government, be given food, shelter or other help by the local administration.

Fire services and other emergency services have orders to leave large metropolitan areas *before* the nuclear strikes occur.

Today, in peace time, Britain's Health Service can only deal with a few hundred cases of very severe burns at any one time. After a nuclear attack there may well be up to a million people suffering from severe burns.

PREPARING FOR A NUCLEAR ATTACK

*Pictures from the British Government Official Handbook
"Protect and Survive"* (H.M. Stationery Office 1980)

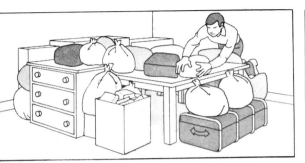 

"The ground burst of a 100 megaton weapon would scoop out a crater 350 feet deep and a mile in diameter . . . *in solid concrete.* And if nice solidly built shelters hundreds of feet deep saved one from the blast, the searing heat and exhaustion of oxygen caused by the fire-storm would trap most survivors within a radius of twenty to sixty miles."

Hanson W. Baldwin, military editor of the *New York Times.*

Experts are convinced that an H-bomb explosion over built-up areas would result in the phenomenon known as a fire-storm. This occurred at Hiroshima and as a result of intensive air raids on Hamburg and Dresden. A fire-storm is a gigantic, uncontrollable fire that sucks in air at hurricane force. This force both feeds and fans the flames until everything is destroyed.

The Police President of Hamburg wrote in his report:

The scenes of terror which took place in the fire-storm area are indescribable. Children were torn away from their parents' hands by the force of the hurricane and whirled into the fire.

People who thought they had escaped fell down, overcome by the devouring force of the heat and died in an instant. . . . A population ready and prepared for the alarm were literally overwhelmed by the fire. . .

That was Hamburg after a heavy raid with conventional bombs; today a single H-bomb might have an explosive force 50,000 times greater than all the bombs used on Hamburg during that raid.

To these facts and these descriptions a sane person can have only one response–it must never happen.

The splitting of the atom has changed everything save our modes of thinking, and thus we drift toward unparalleled catastrophe.

DR ALBERT EINSTEIN

Do the frightening facts about the arms race, which show that we are rushing headlong towards a precipice, make any of those responsible for this disastrous course pull themselves together and reach for the brakes?

The answer is no . . . There are powerful voices around the world who still give credence to the old Roman precept—if you desire peace, prepare for war. This is absolute nuclear nonsense.

LORD LOUIS MOUNTBATTEN

A PERSONAL
POSTSCRIPT

Why does Man today find himself on the very brink of a disaster which could mean the end of all humanity?

Why have the numberless "disarmament conferences" since the first World War *always* ended in failure?

Why, when the two major protagonists already have enough bombs to kill everyone on earth five times over, do they continue to build more and more weaponry?

Why does this obvious madness continue?

First, we must begin to mistrust the "reasonable" men who tell us that our security depends on military power. It is, quite simply, *not true*. We built the A Bomb to give us security; then we built the H Bomb to give us more security. Since then we have the Tridents, the Cruise Missiles and the Russians have the SS20s; but everyone is now less safe than ever before.

The leaders who tell us this are well intentioned. I think they actually believe what they say. But a growing number of people have come to realise, with a rising sense of horror, where, for all their plausibility, these leaders are taking us. Every decision to increase our armaments is justified with carefully documented rhetoric. But they are fooling us, these reasonable men. They haven't delivered what they promised. They continue to tell us that with each accretion of power they are leading us south towards the warm sun of security—yet we find ourselves nearer and nearer to the cold north.

We must begin to mistrust utterly everything these reasonable men say. Just listen with what skilful arguments they attempt to persuade us that only by being "strong" can we find our national safety. Never before has so much precision been attached to so spurious and dangerous a rationality.

The Wrong Focus

The basic cause of our predicament, as I see it, is that we have been looking altogether in the wrong direction. We have been focusing "out there" and not "in here". "Ban the bomb!" we say—yet, if we think about it, the essential danger does not lie in the bomb. It is the human *mind* which gave rise to the bomb. The bomb is but the outward expression of our inner consciousness; it is the precipitation of our inner fear. So *fear*, and not the bomb, is our problem.

A number of years ago, the Natural History Museum in New York reconstructed the evolutionary span of one of those huge extinct Saurians. (It was, if I remember rightly, the Brontosaurus.) One could follow in these models how this animal first began—a much smaller creature—alive, mobile, adaptable. In the course of centuries it grew in size, and then, quite clearly, one could recognize the moment when it became *afraid*. From then on, as fear began to dominate the animal's consciousness, it began to precipitate its fear by developing, like an uncontrollable cancer, its defences—monstrous growths of bone. In time, its entire body became a huge fortress, with small frightened eyes peering through slits in its massive head. So ponderous had it become that it required only a small shift in climatic conditions to render it unviable, and the species became extinct—destroyed by its own fear.

Perhaps there is a lesson here for us humans. We, too, have become a frightened species. Our deep-seated fears have not altered our bodily structure; we have not developed a bone-like covering or tusks or claws. We did not need to for we have precipitated our fear by developing *weapons*. As with the dinosaurs, we act as if we are in the grip of an unconscious and uncontrollable cancer. We gather more and more weapons, many of which we know we cannot use without committing suicide.

The gross size and protective bones of the Brontosaurus were not the real cause of its extinction—but fear; and in the same way it is our fears that are leading us to self-destruction.

What Are We Afraid Of?

Each nation has its own, apparently rational, answer. In the last war, the Soviet Union lost between 30 and 35 million citizens and the most productive industrial areas of the country were totally destroyed. An enormously traumatic national experience, so today they say "Never again!" and they arm themselves accordingly.

The United States, too, is dominated by fear; she is afraid of "Communism" which challenges the very basis of her economic system and she is also afraid of losing her position as "top dog" nation. Britain and other European countries are afraid of being overrun by the enemy if they don't arm themselves. In this way the leaders of these countries play upon the fear of the ordinary people and together the nations perpetuate their policy of armed strength which to each of them appears so valid. Thus, the weapons pile up, the cancer grows, and we move ever closer to the unimaginable fire.

Successive forms of life, not only the dinosaurs, have come and vanished. Is it now Man's turn? Is he also destined to be another of Nature's experiments, to live his span and then be discarded? Or is there a great evolutionary change still possible which may save him? There have been other extraordinary leaps in the past. When the early forms of life, the first amphibians, hesitatingly crawled out of the muddy waters into the air—this was a revolutionary step and it allowed life to continue and enlarge. Now Man must make an equally audacious move if he is to survive. He must learn to look inwards at himself and not "out there" for a solution to his predicament. He must learn *altruism*—which means the opposite of selfishness and defensiveness, a devotion to humanity regardless of all else. It requires us to learn how to trust and not be afraid. *This is the survival imperative of our time.*

"But We MUST Defend Our Freedom and Democracy!"

This is the classic Western justification for "being strong", for the malignant piling up of ever more destructive armaments. We do not often pause to ponder the real meaning of these words. I have come to believe that our idea of freedom, for example, the nurturing of our "individuality" on which we place so high a value, is not what it seems. Our present ideas about freedom derive largely from the 19th-century idea of bourgeois, capitalist freedom—freedom for the new industrial owners to do what they liked, free of any social control. Many learned books have been written in support of this so-called freedom. But it can be expressed very simply—it is a "me-first" philosophy. "Everyone for himself"; "grab what you can", and (so goes the theory) if everybody acted thus society as a whole will benefit.

We have given up this rather crude definition of capitalist ideology, but we are still operating within a "me-first" jungle. In a competitive society the development of what we call individualism is necessary for survival. To get on I *must* push myself, I *must* make more money, etc., and out of this has grown the sacredness of *me*—*my* individuality, *my* creativity, *my* right to do and say what I want, and so on. Is this the only kind of freedom—or, indeed, is it freedom at all?

The concept of individuality which we have developed in the West has very little indeed to do with real freedom. It results in the enclosure, the imprisonment of *me* within myself, with *my* strivings, *my* ambitions, *my* fears, *my* defensiveness, *my* search for security. It is this "me-ness" which creates divisions and alienates me from others; and it can suffocate all that is most tender and trusting in us. In the depths of our consciousness we know this. And how we hate it! The perpetual struggle to compete, to be cleverer than others, to have a better job, to get more money, more comforts—the constant striving of me against others; doing anything to give my ego a boost, knowing that any advance up the ladder of success has to be at the expense of someone else and what we call success is often another form of personal disaster. And we call this freedom!

And what about our democracy—which we are told we must defend even if it means our own suicide? ("Better dead than red".)

The use of the word "democracy" is a powerful agent for the spreading of confusion, double-talk and sheer fakery. Those who control our destinies repeatedly use the word "democracy" for it carries with it an immensely powerful appeal. Words such as "representative Government", the "sovereignty of the people" and so on, exert a profoundly moving effect on us, for they correspond to the deep longing in all of us for a life in which we can co-operate with each other and not compete; a society in which we feel we belong as participating members of a true community, in which we do not have to be competitive or defensive or tough. A society in which we can be free to be really human.

To pretend is always dangerous and if we are to clear our confusions we should understand how far our present "democracy" falls short of what a true democracy might be. Most of us know that we are being bamboozled—and we are inclined to bamboozle ourselves with this wonderful word "democracy". The politicians use it to play upon our fears. They tell us about the terrible dangers that await us if we are not militarily strong and so they *must*, they say, spend more and more of our money on bombs and missiles if "democracy" is to be saved. "Representative Government" is a smoke-screen and not a functional reality. We are allowed every four years to put a cross on a ballot paper for Mr X or Mr Y, and—presto!—we are a "democracy"!

Between us and those who make the great decisions for us there is a wide gap. Today, decisions are taken which affect our lives in the most immediate and intimate way but about which we virtually have no say. We have, for all our talk of "democracy", moved a long way towards becoming a manipulated mass society. It is this which makes individuals feel so powerless and politics so futile.

Our emphasis on the outward forms of democracy—the machinery of voting, the elaborate, archaic rituals of political procedures—allows us to lose sight of the real spirit of democracy. The spirit of democracy is less dependent on legal formulations of government than the quality of human relationship that exists between citizens.

True democracy, if it means anything, means that there exist between people thousands of invisible currents, currents of liking and mutual respect and trust. Without this essential ingredient a "democracy" is but a pile of loose sand.

No country has developed the constitutional, the legal *forms* of political democracy further and with more precision than the United States. But there the essential ingredient is today so eroded that very few Americans dare to walk alone in the streets at night. The outward *forms* remain unchanged—the true spirit of democracy is all but lost.

That is not all.

Our democracy, such as it is, is endangered from another quarter. The democratic instinct which recognizes people as people says nothing about national frontiers. It is unconcerned with them. It pays no more attention to which side of an arbitrary geographic line a man happens to be born on than the colour of his skin, or the way he prays, or his politics. All that is irrelevant. For wherever a man is born, under whatever system, he still shares with us our common humanity. What we share as human beings over-rides all else, and far transcends the differences that at present lead to hostility and hatred.

Today, as a result of our present pathology, we have lost this *universal* sense of democracy. We look across the oceans and see other peoples, not in the light of our common humanity, but almost exclusively in terms of our *fears*—are they *with* us or *against* us? In this way we degrade our feeling about other peoples. We even rejoice when things go wrong with those we happen at this minute to dislike.

What an extraordinary, electrifying change would take place if only we could recapture our sense of common humanity—which is indeed the very heart of true democracy.

In this Crisis of Humanity—To Whom can we Turn?

"We are faced with the most urgent crisis since the dawn of life—tell us to whom we can look for an answer?"

The Politicians? We have already seen how the politicians are misleading us. They believe in military power—with occasional "détentes" or disarmament conferences which have *always* in the past ended in futility.

The Organized Religions? Religious belief systems divide and do not unite us. There are hundreds—perhaps thousands—of religious sects all claiming that they and they alone possess the truth. The religious words they use do not correspond to their actions. For example, for 2,000 years the Christian religion has been preaching humility, gentleness and love. "Love your enemy", they say, and then proceed to demonstrate their love by lending their support to the indiscriminate bombing of men, women and children. The Christian nations on both sides of a war pray to the same God to bring their side victory! And some religious leaders have even given their blessing to the planes that will deliver death and unbelievable suffering to whole populations.

Organized religions have provided us with escapes from reality. "Have 'faith'", they say, and they extend false comfort. We have listened in vain for a united clarion call from all the organized religions of the world for humanity to come to its senses.

The Educators? Education does not address itself to the crisis of human survival but to the training of children to achieve personal advancement. Education plays it safe; it won't rock the boat; it helps to maintain the *status quo*.

The Scientists? They concern themselves with the gathering of more and more information about our environment. Much of this has been immensely useful, much of it has no relevance whatever to our human needs. An enormous number of scientists are actually assisting in the perfection of instruments of mass destruction.

The Revolutionaries? They believe that in changing the outward condition of society, men and nations will live in harmony and peace. To substitute one social-economic system by another has, in some cases, brought great human betterment. But unless it is accompanied by an inner revolution within people themselves, the revolution will soon be subverted and international hostilities will be as great as ever. We have seen how, in every revolution, to follow the "correct line", the right formula and dogma, becomes more important than people.

*   *   *

What is the reason for this great failure to give us help? Every belief system, every intellectual theory, every political "*ism*" represents an attempt to give us the answer. But Life is an ever changing, flowing process. Life cannot be imprisoned in any theory, and every attempt to do so only leads, in the end, to disappointment, cynicism and a pervading sense of futility.

Thus there are no authorities, no systems, no leaders, no experts, no religious beliefs to whom we can look to bring us back from the brink of extinction. Our reaction is to blame others. Internationally the United States blames Russia, Russia blames the United States and we blame our politicians! And in our personal lives is it not the same? "If only *he* was different!" "If only *she* would change!"

So what, or whom, are we left with? The answer stirs and frightens us. We are left with ourselves as individuals, and only ourselves. So accustomed have we become to look to others—the experts, the intellectuals, the religious—that we assiduously avoid a sense of personal responsibility. Yet the world is as it is because of the way we think, feel and act. If this is true, then I must look inward to myself to see how *I* think, feel and act, and cease to hope that others will find the answer for me.

"We Are Copies"

Before we look to ourselves to discover how we feel, think and act, we must become clear as to who we *are*. When I write "we are copies" what am I driving at?

I have come to realize that so many of my thoughts, my conclusions, my scale of values, are not really "mine" at all. They have been handed down to me by the way I was conditioned.

I see the world through the distorting lens of my particular coloured spectacles and (until I become aware of this) I feel completely convinced that what I see is *just like that*, that what I see is objective reality. I am English so I happen to see the world as an Englishman sees it. It is a little un-nerving to realize that if I had been born a Russian, a Chinese, a Frenchman, my world-view would be wholly different—but I would be just as convinced that what I saw represented reality. This is true of everyone.

Not only are we conditioned by our nationality, but by our class, our upbringing, our education, by the loyalties which are considered noble, by the prevailing moralities and customs of our society, and so on. All these were instilled in us from the moment that we were born. That is why I say that we are second-hand, that is, we are copies.

It takes an effort, and at first an uncomfortable one, to realize how deeply, how subtly, we are conditioned. How little is really "mine"—authentically mine. I think of all the grand conclusions that I have over the years enunciated with such confidence and on which I based all my psychological security!

Conditioning influences every aspect of our lives—and especially, and most dangerously, it convinces me that "my" way, "my" country is *right*. The sense of national superiority, brain-washed into us when we were too young to resist, has become unconsciously a central part of the very structure of our thinking and feeling. It is a sentiment that divides and does not bridge; and in the end it inevitably leads to war.

It is quite obvious that each country has its own historical traditions and customs, its own special skills, its own humour and art, its own celebrations. I delight in this variety, these differences. But what is enormously dangerous is the belief that our particular country is somehow superior, cleverer, more "sensible", less selfish, more peace-loving than any other. We are not talking about practising "tolerance" towards people of other nationalities, or of another colour of skin, for "tolerance" *always* denotes an unacknowledged sense of superiority. People everywhere are people— it is as simple as that.

Nationalism is another form of racism, and nationalism is a twin brother of "patriotism". Racism and nationalism are a poison which prevents us from understanding others and from seeing the world as it is. Patriotic people will consider this blasphemy, but that is not important. What is important is to discover for ourselves whether or not it is true.

Where Do I Come In?

I mean this question literally. Where do I, the writer of this book, come in? If what I have written is true, where do you, the reader, come in? As mere individuals what can we *do* against the enormous political and industrial pressures, the international rivalries, that are driving us towards disaster?

Yes, we must continue to protest as loudly and distinctly as we can against the direction our leaders are taking us; and against their double-talk and their absurd attempts to persuade us that even if there is a nuclear attack we can "survive".

Protest, however necessary, is still "out there". I must start much closer to home—that is, with myself, for society is a projection of myself writ large. If I remain a "me first" person I will only be lending my support to a "me first" society. If I am fearful, I will only add to the sum total of our collective fears.

The word "fear" covers a wide spectrum—there are fears hidden from my consciousness much more subtle than the fear, say, of being over-run by the Russians. I have to listen very carefully to my feelings and reveries to discover the extraordinary extent to which my actions are influenced by fear. Fear of insecurity, fear of what others may think, fear of failure, fear of change, fear of not being loved—and a host of other hidden fears. I find I must also listen to myself carefully to become aware of just how much I am a conditioned being, a second-hand being, how many of my opinions and conclusions on which I have based my life are not authentically mine at all. I am so quick to pass judgements, to condemn or praise (all based on these "opinions".). "That's good", "That's wrong", "He's stupid", "She's talking through her hat".

By passing these quick, almost reflex, judgements I interpose my own pre-conceived ideas and prejudices even before I have time to listen carefully to what is being said. To this extent my judgements are false judgements. In the same way I pass judgement on myself. If I'm angry, fearful or jealous, I quickly condemn it as being "wrong". So I never come face to face with what I am. I never say that that anger is *me*, that that jealousy is *me*, that that fear is *me*. If I could only listen, really listen, to others and myself without condemning or glorifying, I might begin to understand myself and how I think and feel. Over and over again, since the earliest days of history, we have been told that to *know oneself* is the beginning of wisdom. Thus I must listen to myself and others—listen as I might to music, just listen, and with that quality of listening I may begin to know myself and learn just how far I am myself contributing to the confusion and violence in the world.

What has all this to do with the enormous danger that today confronts mankind? It has *directly* to do with it. We must each start where we are. Lasting order and peace will only come about when the individual takes full responsibility for his own feelings, thoughts and actions. When the individual, you and me, sets about to alter *within himself* the causes which produce violence and hate, only then shall we have a chance of survival. We must start making a difference where we are.

To know oneself is not as easy as it sounds. Our self-protective mind slips and slides and cheats whenever we get near to a defensive nerve. It requires no less than a readiness to revolutionize our way of thinking. If we become aware of how we feel, think and act, then we will begin to understand why societies act as they do. When we have cut the rope that has tied us to our conditioned responses and severed ourselves from the hope that others will give us the answer, then for the first time we come face to face with reality, with *what is*; and that is the beginning of real freedom, freedom even from our fears.

The one thing the leaders of the world have never tried is to *trust*, because most of us have not tried it either. Yet trust breeds trust as surely as hate breeds hate. Individually and collectively we must come to understand that *truth is always positive*, for it allows us to shed our evasions and pretensions, the numberless "shoulds" and "should nots" that burden us; and the whole confused mass of our self-justifications. When we begin to understand ourselves we stand on rock and can start from there.

The Life energy that is now spent on self-protection and violence is precisely the same Life energy that can give us a world of co-operation and affection. So how each individual feels, thinks and acts is of supreme importance in this world crisis. The solution, if we could only understand it, is not "out there" but within ourselves.